It was a frosty Boxing Day at Santa's snowy house.
Nobody was stirring, nope, not even Moe the mouse.

Santa Claus was sleeping soundly, snoring in his chair.
His tummy full to bursting with the mince pies stuffed in there.

The reindeer were all watching 'Deerstenders' in the stables.
Mrs Claus had fallen asleep whilst clearing up the table.

When suddenly...
BUUUURRP!
Santa's tummy griped and groaned:
"Enough is quite enough!
After all those nice mince pies
I'm really rather stuffed!"
"I need to get some exercise,
and plenty of fresh air.
The sprouts are really foul down here
- it's a nasty niff nightmare!
Fire away me hearties!
Someone open a window!
THIS WAY TO BOTTOM

"You're right," sighed Santa, rubbing his bulging tummy.
"It's wobbling and grumbling, and starting to feel funny!"

"Besides, today is Boxing Day - our work is not yet done...
There's still ANOTHER sack of gifts to take for lots more fun!"

"What MORE presents - just for me?" I hear you children cry.
Hold your reindeers, girls and boys...stop peering at the sky.

Those presents aren't for children, hmmm, well, not quite.
Then who? Who else can't sleep for excitement tonight...?

Santa packed a midnight snack of sarnies (turkey melt),
Sausage, cake, a box of chocs and then undid his belt!

So, kissing Mrs Claus with his hat wedged on his head,
Santa went to stir the worn-out reindeer from their bed.

The reindeer were now snoring in their itchy piles of hay,
"Wake up!" bellowed Santa. "Let's make some little uns' day!"

But Rudolph's sleepy gang weren't keen to leave their beds...
So he dangled a carrot smoothie over their greedy heads.

So who else has been naughty? Who else has been nice?
(Watch out Santa, not so fast - you'll slip on all that ice!)

Why, lots of little ANIMALS also love to see
Lots of shiny presents underneath THEIR Christmas tree!

With sat nav at the ready, to the jungle Santa soars,
To a little cub called Max who is shy of making roars.

Santa left the bashful cub a handy megaphone,
So now sweet Max's roars can make his family groan.

Santa gave the muddy hippo a blow-up crocodile...
To roll with in the wallow - oh, it really makes her smile.

The cheeky little monkey loved his whizzy-weeeee trapeze,
So the mischief-making monkey can swing round and round the trees.

Then, Santa left the elephant a handy mobile phone,
(Well, noisy trunk calls really make the other creatures moan).

Santa gave the snappy croc an electric buzzing toothbrush,
If bits of hippo stick in his teeth - it really makes him blush!

Next, Santa and the reindeer jingled off towards the sea,
But not before he'd had his flask of mince pie-flavoured tea.

With goggles, wet suits, rubber rings and flippers on their feet,
They gurgled down and down, sinking really, reeeeaaaally deep.

For the bubbly, cuddly octopus, a present for each hand...
Eight percussion instruments to start a one-'man' band.

Santa left the baby shark a wooden log to chew,
Hopefully he'll prefer THAT to nibbling me and you!

Then, Santa gave the dolphin a camera so he can pose,
(He's famous for that cheesy grin under his bottle nose).

The jiggly jellyfish received a hula hoop to wobble,
Oh, and some strawberry jelly which she really loves to gobble.

The next stop on their journey was the desert full of sand,
It was slippery like snow, the sleigh was difficult to land!

Santa gave the chameleon a box of fancy dress,
With cowboy, nurse and spaceman suits she surely would impress.

Then, Santa left the greedy vulture a gold knife, fork and bib,
To help improve his table manners when feasting on spare rib.

Santa gave the grumpy camel a hamper stuffed with food,
Well, eating hump fat every day puts her in a baaaad mood!

Next, Santa gave the knobbly warthog a face-pack made of mud.
It made her feel so pretty, plus it tasted like choccy pud.

Then Santa left the nervous meerkat some binoculars to see
If that hungry baby vulture was coming here for tea!

Off they jingled to the farm, where the foal got black tap shoes.
She loves to make 'clip-clop, clip-clops' with her noisy hooves.

Recipe for UNDERWEAR STEW

1 pair of underpants (washed of course!)

2 pairs of socks (stripy preferably)

1 string vest

2 pairs of granny's knickers

ketchup (as required)

The kid goat loved her cook book, packed with lots of tasty meals...
Using items from the washing line that she likes to steal!

Santa left the restless lambs each a fluffy teddy...
Instead of counting humans at night, they can cuddle them in beddy.

Next, Santa left the cute duckling a yellow rubber toy,
To play with in her big bath-pond - it looked just like a boy!

The calves received moo-pods to play their favourite songs -
Well, chewing grass dawn till dusk makes the day seem loooong.

Then, Santa left the piglets lots of cushions, plants and flowers,
They're actually quite sty-proud - hey, they even take hot showers!

Santa left the fluffy chicks a camouflage disguise...
In case that naughty fox springs a horrible surprise!

Quickly, Santa left a book on anger for the bull,
Wary of his bright red suit, Santa hollered "PUUUUUULL!"

Luckily, Santa just escaped a 'present' on his sleigh...
Next year, that traffic warden won't have any toys to play!

Oh what fun it was to ride, 'til out came the thermal vests,
For where they're heading now will freeze the hairs upon their chests.

He gave a karaoke machine to the canines famed for howling,
The arctic wolves love to sing...though it leaves the walrus scowling.

Then, Santa left the polar bear an inflatable rubber boat,
So when the icecaps finally melt, she has somewhere left to float.

Next, Santa left the hungry penguins a fishing rod or two,
The icy water makes them wrinkly - sometimes they go blue!

Santa gave the cool dude seals snowboards to whizz around...
When your tummy is that big it's hard to leave the ground.

Yikes, Santa - after hours at work - reeeeeeally needed the loo,
He jingled (gently!) to your house, where he did a - ooh, never mind, you!

To the spider sliding in your bath, Santa gave a handy ladder,
Trying to escape the slippy bath was driving him madder and madder.

Santa gave the rascal rats playing "Hopscotch" by the bins,
A bag of stinky, rotting food - you've never seen such grins!

Then, for the rabbit in your garden, Santa left a black top hat.
She conjured with her carrot wand, a wee man, just like that.

Santa gave the grateful hedgehog a stick-on fire alarm,
So, come next Bonfire Night, she will not come to any harm.

The arty squirrel gave kisses galore for the oil set for his tail.
He paints great works of art to flog to the house-proud snail.

Hoorah, at last the sleigh was empty, but so was Santa's tummy,
And when poor Santa's hungry - GRUUMMMBLE - he really isn't funny.

The reindeer, too, were pooped, and on their floppy, tired last legs.
To the grotto they all hobbled off for tea and scrambled eggs.

Rudolph and his buddies staggered to their beds of hay,
Too tired to spot something still at the bottom of the sleigh.

Wow! Santa came with one last gift: foot spas for their paws.
Well, after running 10,000 miles wouldn't your feet be sore?

THE END until next year!

Santa's Naughty List

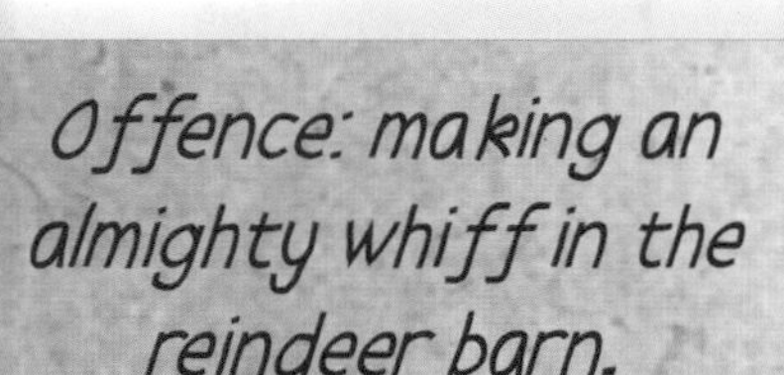

Offence: making an almighty whiff in the reindeer barn.

Offence: scoffing all Grandpa Claus's lettuces.

Offence: making Santa's nose more red than Rudolph's.

Offence: nibbling Santa's toes when he went for a paddle.

Offence: over-enthusiastic cuddling!

Offence: not laughing at Santa's hilarious jokes.